Kelli

Kelli

cinthia

Brittany Ackard

Amber

Kevin

V.

Kevin

Antonette

Kevin

Kevin

cinthia

LIFE SERIES

Love Your Neighbor

Level 7
Seventh-day Adventist Readers

Patricia A. Habada

Sally J. McMillan

Blossom Engen

Frances Blahovich

Mitzi J. Smith

Acknowledgments

Grateful acknowledgment is made to the following:

Ginn and Company for assistance in the preparation of this book; and to Rosly Walter, Ginn staff editor, for guidance.

Reading steering committee members: Marion Hartlein, chairman; Patricia Habada, secretary; Frances Clark, Southwestern Conference; Erna Hauck, Columbia Union College; Sandra Herndon, Northeastern Conference; Elizabeth Hudak, Florida Conference; Erma Lee, North Pacific Union; Norwida Marshall, Southern Union; Lorraine Miller, Oregon Conference; Joyce Morse, Southern California Conference; Esther Novak, Wisconsin Conference; Desmond Rice, Southern College; Aleene Schaeffer, Union College; George Unger, Canadian Union.

Canadian consultants: Herbert Penney-Flynn, Newfoundland; Frances Schander, Saskatchewan; George Unger, Ontario.

Special consultants: Margaret Hafner, New York; Betty McCune, Loma Linda University; Millie Youngberg, Andrews University.

Grateful acknowledgment is made to the following publishers, authors, and agents for permission to use and adapt copyrighted materials:

Doubleday & Company for "Mice" from *Fifty-One Nursery Rhymes* by Rose Fyleman. Copyright © 1931, 1932 by Doubleday & Company, Inc. Reprinted by permission of the publisher.

Grosset & Dunlap, Inc. for "Sudden Storm" by Elizabeth Coatsworth. Reprinted by permission of Grosset & Dunlap, Inc. from *The Sparrow Bush* by Elizabeth Coatsworth. Copyright © 1966 by Grosset & Dunlap, Inc.

D. C. Heath for "No Smiles Today" by Kathleen Barabas. From *Marching Along.* Copyright © 1980 by D. C. Heath. Used by permission of D. C. Heath.

Harper & Row Publishers, Inc. for "The Snake" from *Dogs and Dragons, Trees and Dreams; A Collection of Poems* by Karla Kuskin. Copyright © 1958 by Karla Kuskin. Reprinted by permission of Harper & Row Publishers, Inc.

Jan-Lee Music for "God Made Our Hands" by Jill Jackson and Sy Miller. Copyright © 1959. Used by permission of Jan-Lee Music.

Bertha Klausner International Literary Agency for "Automobile Mechanics" from *I Like Machinery* by Dorothy A. Baruch. Copyright © 1933 by Harper & Brothers, New York. Permission granted by Bertha Klausner International Literary Agency.

Macmillan Publishing Company for "Maxie." Adapted with permission of Four Winds Press, an imprint of Macmillan Publishing Company, from *Maxie* by Mildred Kantrowitz. Text, copyright © 1970 by Mildred Kantrowitz.

Patricia Miles Martin for "Fox and the Fire" by Miska Miles.

David McCord for "Song of the Train" by David McCord. Copyright © 1952 by David McCord. Used by permission of the author.

Modern Curriculum Press, Inc. for *Henry* by Elizabeth Vreeken. Copyright © 1959 by Modern Curriculum Press, Inc. Used by permission of Modern Curriculum Press, Inc.

Barbara Owen Webb for "Katie's Swimming Pool" adapted from *Katie's Swimming Pool for Sparrows* by Barbara Owen Webb. Reprinted from Humpty Dumpty's Magazine by permission of the author. Copyright © 1976 by Parents' Magazine Enterprises, a division of Gruner/Jahr, U.S.A., Inc.

Illustrations and photographs were provided by the following: Ron Church—Photography Unlimited (115, 119); Tom Cooke (8–44); Trish Dinkle Crowe (220–223, 245); Jeffrey Dever (224); Leo and Diane Dillon (128–129, 137–140, 143–149); Len Ebert (130–136); Jeff Foott—Bruce Coleman, Inc., New York (116, 118, 120–123); Sasha Georgevitch (190–198); Ted Lewin (48–54, 63–76); Annie Lunsford (168–175); David M. McPhail (88–114); Angela Moizio-Ackerman (225–231); Les Morrill (84); Bob Owens (164); Pauline Perry (176); Bradley O. Pomeroy (177–188); Ted Rand (199–203); H. Armstrong Roberts (219); Mary Rumford (150–156); John Schoenherr (247–261); Joel Snyder (55–62, 157–163); Richard Steadham (208–218); Arvis Steward (77–83, 85); Earl Thollander (189); Jeanne Turner (232–244); Stan Wayman—Photo Researchers, Inc. (117).

The unit introduction pages were designed by Gregory Fosella Associates. Cover design by Dennis Feree. Cover photo by David B. Sherwin. Dever Designs provided consultation services in art and design.

Contents

6

The Dog Next Door

The Bradleys Move In

   William and Lucy Brown sat
on their steps, watching a big van.
   The van was coming along the street.
It stopped at the house next door.
A woman was waiting there in the doorway.
   New people were going to move in. Someone
was coming to live in the house next door.

Two movers began to take a big basket
out of the moving van.

"Put that big basket over there, please,"
the woman said. "That's fine."

"I hope a girl moves in there," Lucy said.
Lucy's big cat was sitting on her lap.

William was thinking about the new people.
He hoped there would be a boy in the family.

"I'm going over there and ask if there is a boy
in the family," William said. "You stay here, Lucy."
But Lucy followed him.

The movers were going up the front walk with a big box.

"You can take that box to the back door," the woman said.

The movers took the box. William and Lucy waited by the front door till the woman looked at them and smiled.

"Hello," she said. "Do you live around here?"

"Yes. We live next door," William said.

"I'm Mrs. Bradley. Stanley will be pleased to have you next door."

William was happy.

"There's a BOY in the family," he thought.

10

Mrs. Bradley was still talking.
"Mr. Bradley and Stanley will be coming
very soon."

Along the street came a little car
with a man in it. A great big dog
sat beside him. The car stopped
in front of the house and the dog barked
and jumped out.

WOOF
WOOF

"THAT'S Stanley?" William said.
"Stanley is a **Dog?**"

Stanley was barking as he came up the walk.
Everyone could see that Stanley was very happy.
And everyone could see that Lucy's cat
and William were not happy at all.

11

The cat jumped down and climbed into an oak tree.
When Stanley barked, the cat climbed higher.

The movers came up the walk
with a big doghouse.

Stanley was still barking,
and the cat climbed still higher.
Up she went—higher—still higher—

"Someone will have to get that cat
down from the tree," Mr. Bradley said.

"The cat will come down," Lucy said.
"She knows about that oak tree."

The movers looked at Mrs. Bradley.
"We are almost finished. Everything is
in the house but this. Where does it go?"

"Move the doghouse back by the fence, please,"
Mrs. Bradley said.

Stanley followed them around back.
Lucy's cat came down from the oak tree
and ran home.

When the movers came back, Stanley came too,
and jumped up on William.

"Say, Mrs. Bradley," William said.
"Would it be all right if I take Stanley
for a walk?"

"Stanley would like that very much,"
Mrs. Bradley said.

William and Stanley and Lucy went
down the street.

"This is where OUR family lives, Stanley,"
Lucy said. "We live here with our mother
and father. And the cat that climbed
up in your oak tree was MY cat.
You and the cat have to be friends."

"Stanley doesn't know about talk,"
William said.

"How do you know?" Lucy asked.

William didn't know how to answer.
He thought about this for a long time.

Stanley was having a good time.
Every now and then he ran away, looking
in people's gardens. But each time,
he came right back and walked beside William.
William was feeling better now.

"This is a nice dog," William said. "It's
almost as good as having a boy next door."

"It's not almost as good as having a boy
next door," Lucy said. "It's better."

Things I Like

I like a little ladybug
Crawling on my thumb,
I like a little humming-bird,
Hum-hum-hum-

I like a little sea shell,
And dandelion fuzz,
Or a brave little bumble-bee,
Buzz-buzz-buzz-

I like a little lizard
Hiding in the dark,
But most, I like a puppy,
Bark-bark-bark.

Patricia Miles Martin

16

It Looks Like Rain

"William," Mrs. Brown said.
"I want you to put your raincoat on
when you go to school today.
It looks like rain."

She looked at Lucy. This was Lucy's
first week of school. "And Lucy,
I want you to put your raincoat on too."

"I don't need a raincoat," Lucy said.
"I can take my umbrella."

"Put your raincoat on and take your umbrella
too," their mother said.

William went to get the raincoats
and an umbrella.

Lucy put on her raincoat. She looked
at the umbrella.

"This is the old one," she said.
"It has holes in it and rain comes right through.
I'll get all wet when the rain comes through."

Lucy liked having an umbrella to carry
in the rain, but she didn't want to carry one
with holes that would let the rain through.
She went to find her new one.

When William and Lucy opened the front door,
Stanley, the dog next door, was waiting.
He decided that he would walk to school
with William and Lucy.

Stanley jumped around, wanting to carry
something. William decided to let him carry
his book bag.

Stanley went off carrying it proudly.
Proudly, Lucy walked with him,
carrying the new umbrella. She wished
it would rain so she could open it.

When they got to school, Stanley put
the book bag on the steps and went back home.

All through the day, Lucy wished for rain.

When it was time to go home from school,
Miss Little said, "Don't forget to put on
your raincoats, and don't forget to take
your umbrellas. There is a gray cloud
in the sky and it looks like rain."

Outside, Lucy looked up at the sky.
The sky was blue-gray. There was a big gray cloud
up there, but it wasn't raining.

Then Lucy looked down the street
and saw Stanley coming to meet her.

He jumped around, wanting to carry something.

"I don't have a thing that you can carry
but my umbrella," Lucy said.

Stanley was still jumping.

Lucy decided to let him carry
her new umbrella.

"All right, Stanley," she said.
"Stop jumping. Here. Take it."

Proudly, Stanley took the umbrella.

Lucy and Stanley started home.

When they were almost home, it started to rain.

"Let me have my umbrella," Lucy said to Stanley.

Stanley backed away.

Lucy started to take the umbrella from Stanley,
but Stanley tugged at it.

"DROP IT," Lucy said. "DROP IT."

Lucy knew that Stanley was not going to drop it.

Lucy's friends were coming along the street.

They all had their umbrellas open but Lucy.

At last Jane Ann came along.

"You can walk under MY umbrella," she said.
"Two of us can fit under it."

They started down the street. Stanley
trotted along, carrying Lucy's umbrella.

The next morning, Lucy went outside to look
at the sky. There was a gray cloud up there,
a very big gray cloud. She decided
that it looked like rain.

Stanley was waiting on the walk.

"I'll have to take my umbrella to school,"
Lucy said to her mother.

"And don't forget to put your raincoat on,"
her mother said.

"I won't forget." Lucy picked up two umbrellas—
her own new one, and the old one.

"What are you going to do with that old umbrella?"
William asked.

"I have decided to let Stanley have it," she said.
"He can have the old umbrella for his own—
his very own!"

23

They started down the street.

Proudly, Stanley was carrying his own old umbrella.

When they were almost there, it started to rain.

Lucy opened her own new umbrella.

She listened to the drops of rain
on her umbrella.

She listened to the swish—swish—swish of water
when cars went by.

She listened to friends calling to each other.

It was a fine morning.

She and William hurried on to school.

Sudden Storm

The rain comes in sheets
Sweeping the streets,
Here, here, and here,
Umbrellas appear,
Red, blue, yellow, green,
They tilt and they lean
Like mushrooms, like flowers
That grow when it showers.

Elizabeth Coatsworth

25

William Gets His Hair Cut

William Brown needed to have his hair cut.

"Here is money to get your hair cut,"
his father said. "If you hurry back home, I will
take you and Lucy to the Pathfinder Fair today."

William decided to hurry.

He wanted to go to the Pathfinder Fair.

William got on his bicycle and started
down the street to go to the barber shop.
Lucy was calling Stanley, the dog next door,
but Stanley decided to follow William's bicycle.

William parked his bicycle outside
the barber shop. Stanley began to push
into the shop ahead of William.

"You stay outside," William said. "I will not
be gone long."

He went inside and sat down to wait.
There were four men ahead of him.

William could see Stanley through the window.
Stanley wanted to find another way
to get inside the barber shop. He went
into the shoe shop next door.

Pretty soon Stanley came rushing out.
A woman was running after him.

She looked in the window of the barber shop
and then opened the door.

"Where did that big dog come from?" she asked.

Everyone looked at William.

"He's not MY dog," William said.

"Well, that dog jumped in my window
and walked all over my shoes," she said.

The woman shut the door with a bang.
William watched through the window.
The woman went back to her shop,
and Stanley lay down on the sidewalk
in front of the barber shop.

28

Three men came to get their hair cut,
but Stanley barked at them.

The barber looked at William. "Boy," he said,
"isn't that your dog?"

William looked at his shoes. "No," he said.
"He just followed me. He lives next door
to my house."

"Well," the barber said. "That dog is keeping
people out of my shop. There are people here
ahead of you, but I'll cut your hair now.
I don't want that dog around here.
Get up in the chair. Hurry."

William got up in the chair, and the barber
moved the chair around and started to work.

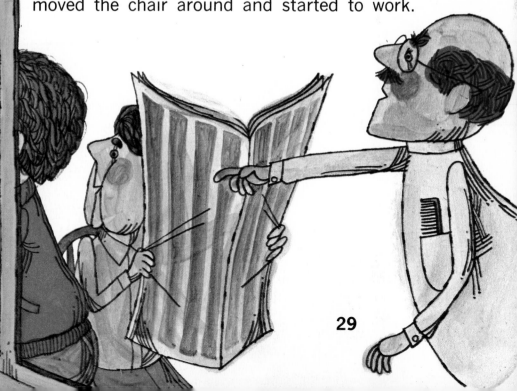

29

William's hair fell everywhere.

No one had ever cut William's hair
in such a hurry.

The barber moved the chair around again,
and William got down. He gave the money
to the barber and went outside
and got on his bicycle.

He rode home as fast as he could go,
and Stanley ran ahead of him.

Lucy was on the front steps.

"Dad's waiting for us inside," she said.

His father looked at William's hair.

"It looks fine," he said. "You weren't gone long. That's what a boy can do when he decides to hurry. We have a lot of time to get to the Pathfinder Fair."

"He's going some place, so that's why he hurried," Lucy said.

"It's the barber who hurried most of all," said William.

At the Fair Lucy sat on one side of her father, and William sat on the other side.

The wind was cool on the back of William's neck.

William and the Doghouse

William Brown walked into the house
just as his mother picked up the telephone.

"Hello . . . . oh yes, Mrs. Bradley . . . .
to camp meeting? Is that so? . . . . Well, well . . . .
Yes, William will do that for you . . . . Don't be
worried about a thing."

William waited until she set the telephone down.

"What did Mrs. Bradley say? Why did you say
'don't be worried'? What do I have to do?"

"The Bradleys are going to camp meeting
for a week or so, and Mrs. Bradley wanted to know
if you will take care of their yard
and pick up the mail while they are away—"
William waited until she finished talking.
"—And," his mother said, "she wanted to know
if you will take care of the dog too."
"I would LIKE to take care of Stanley!"
William said. "And I'll take care of their yard
and everything too."

33

William hurried out of the house and ran across
his own yard and over to the Bradleys' back door.

Mrs. Bradley showed him what to feed the dog,
and then she showed him how to water the grass.

"Don't be worried about a thing," William said.
"I'll take care of the yard and of Stanley, too."

"I know you will," Mrs. Bradley said.

"I think I'll take Stanley's doghouse across the yard
to OUR house, while you're gone," said William.

Everyone waved good-by when Mr. and Mrs. Bradley went away in their car.

All the girls and boys in the block helped William move the doghouse across the yard.

Stanley went with them.

"This dog knows a lot," William said. "He knows 'want-to-go-for-a-walk' and 'where's-the-cat.'"

At last the doghouse was set in William's yard by the back door.

William knew that everything would be fine.

35

When night came, Stanley sat on the grass looking worried. William showed him the doghouse.

"Don't be worried, Stanley," William said. "It's the same old doghouse. Go on in."

Stanley backed away.

William decided that Stanley didn't know what to do and that he would have to show him. William crawled into the doghouse.

Stanley crawled in too.

But now William couldn't get out.

He pushed at Stanley, but Stanley thought William was playing and Stanley pushed back.

William was worried.

36

William wanted to get outside, but Stanley
was in his way. He called for help.

"DAD. help. LUCY. MOM."

But no one answered.
It was getting hot in the doghouse,
and William was worried. He didn't know what to do.
He thought he would have to stay there all night.

Then he thought of something.

"Stanley," he said. "Where's the cat?
Where's the cat?"

Stanley got up at once and crawled outside
to look for the cat.

William crawled outside too.

"Come on, Stanley," William said.
"You can sleep on the floor by my bed tonight."
They went into the house. William showed Stanley
where to sleep. "There. Down on the floor,"
William said. "Down, Stanley!"

Stanley went to sleep on the floor
and didn't move until morning.

The next morning, William's friends helped
carry the doghouse across the yard
and back to the Bradleys' yard.

The Bradleys Come Home

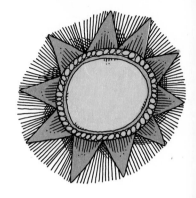

It was Sunday, and William
was watering the Bradleys' grass.

"You have all the fun," Lucy said.
"You get to take care of Stanley,
and you get to water the grass too.
And I only get to watch. Let me water."

"All right," William said. "You can
water. But keep the hose still so the water
doesn't flip all over the place."

"All right," said Lucy.
"I'll do exactly as you say."

Lucy was standing with her back
against the oak tree. She took
the hose and held it still
for a long time.

Then she gave it one flip.

"You heard me tell you not to flip
the water around," William said.

"I heard," Lucy said.

"Then stop it. You got water
all over me," William said. "Stop it."

So Lucy gave the hose one
more flip.

William looked at Stanley, who was sleeping
under the oak tree.

Lucy took a long time to water
the grass. The grass looked nice and green.

Stanley woke up and walked over to William.
He pushed against William and then
wagged his tail. William gave him a pat,
and Stanley's tail wagged faster.

Mr. and Mrs. Bradley would be home
from camp meeting any time now. They did not
come home that day, but next morning William heard
Stanley barking. He heard a car door shut with a bang.
Then he heard the other car door. He hurried outside.

Stanley jumped around and wagged his tail.

Mrs. Bradley took a basket into the house.
Mr. Bradley took a box out of the back
of the car.

Mrs. Bradley called to Mr. Bradley,
"Better call William right away!"

"William's here," Mr. Bradley called back.
"Hello there, William. Everything looks fine. Nice work,
William. We knew you would do a good job."

William was very pleased. "I liked doing it,"
he said.

"Mrs. Bradley and I have something for you,
William. It's a surprise. Your mother and father
said you could have it. We thought
you would be pleased. Come on in."

William and Stanley followed Mr. Bradley
into the house.

There in a basket was a little puppy.

"We knew you would like him," Mrs. Bradley said.
"Someday this puppy will look just like Stanley."

At first, William didn't know what to say.
Then he knew.

"It's just exactly what I want," he said.

"We knew you would like him," Mrs. Bradley said.

"There's only one thing better than having
a dog next door," William said, "and that's having
a dog of your very own."

He picked up the puppy. It pushed against
William and licked his chin. And then it wagged
its tail, exactly as Stanley did.

What Happens Now?

Vowel Puzzles

Think of one vowel letter which can fit into all the blanks in one sentence. Then read the sentence.

1. Th_s sh_p w_ll take a tr_p.

2. The t_p is n_t in the b_x.

3. D_d c_n n_p on his b_ck.

4. A bird can s_ng and flap its w_ngs.

5. T_d m_t a h_n with a b_ll on her n_ck.

6. A d_ck having f_n in the s_n began

to r_n.

7. A tr_tting horse named D_t st_pped on

the t_p of a hill.

8. D_ck sl_d and h_t h_s sh_n.

9. N_n s_t on t_n s_nd, then r_n b_ck

to the l_nd.

Reviewing the generalization that the vowel sound is usually short in words of the CVC, CCVC, and CVCC spelling patterns

45

It Is Time

47

A Little Patch of Back Yard

Jonathan Mack's father was going to paint the back steps.

"I'll go with you," Jonathan said.

They walked outside, and Jonathan sat down in the back yard.

Ants were marching through the grass
in a long parade. Jonathan lay down
on his stomach to watch.

Pill bugs curled up into little balls,
and beetles crawled under little rocks.

One small brown beetle climbed
up a blade of grass. It fell off
and lay on its back
and kicked its legs in the air.

Jonathan turned it over, and
the beetle hurried away.

Down came a robin. The robin tipped
its head this way and that.

"The robin hears a worm in the ground,"
Jonathan said.

"H'm," said his father.
He stopped to look.
The robin tugged and tugged.

Then—there came Mrs. Fell's cat.

The cat came creeping—creeping—slow—slow.

"Watch that cat!" Jonathan's father said.

"I'll watch," said Jonathan.

"I won't let it get in the paint."

SWISH—

A jay darted down over the cat's head.
The cat jumped back. Away it went—
up and over the fence.

"Cat's gone," Jonathan said.

Away went the robin.
And away went the jay.

The little ants were still marching
in their long parade.

Jonathan's father had been working
a long time. "Well," he said,
"I've finished my paint job."
He sat down beside Jonathan.
"Time to rest," he said.

A beetle lit on Mr. Mack's hand,
and he watched it a while.

"One patch of back yard is like a
little world," Jonathan said. "Right
here I can see all kinds of things
that God has made. I can see grass,
and an ant parade
marching through the grass.
I can see worms, and birds digging for food.
God made all these things,
and He put them all in my backyard."

"H'm," said his father.
"I was just painting.
I didn't see all those things."

Father smiled at Jonathan.
"Where is that ant parade?" he asked.
"Come on. I'll show you," said Jonathan.

54

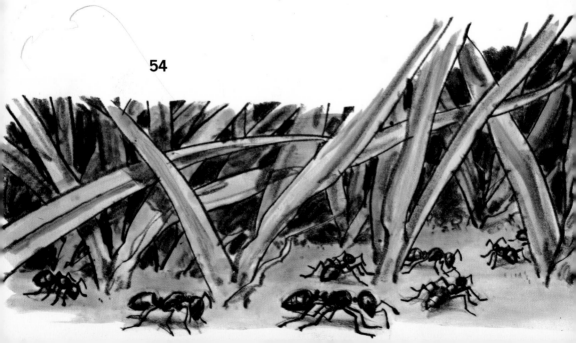

I Walk the Long Way

I leave the hogan in the morning.
I walk the long way to the bus stop.
The morning is beautiful.

A quail sits on her nest under the cactus—
small quail-nest under the cactus.
Quietly I walk. Quietly.

I wait here at the bus stop.
Blue sky is over me.
Yellow-brown sand is under my feet.
The land is beautiful.
I hear the rattle of the school bus.
The school bus stops for me.

It is time to sit and listen to my teacher.

I learn a new language.

I laugh and my teacher laughs with me.

Now I take the long way back to the hogan.
Quietly, the quail sits
on the nest
under the cactus.
I walk softly.

I am home.

I take a pail of water to the field—

a pail of water for the corn—

a pail of water for the thirsty corn.

The sunset is beautiful.

The moon is high.

It is time to sit and listen to the old ones.

It is time to learn the stories of my people.

The words are beautiful.

A cloud hides the moon.
I hear a coyote calling in the night—
coyote calling in the black night.
The night is beautiful.

A Night in the Mountains

Jennifer West and her mother and
father were on their way to stay
in the mountains for a night.

"We'll be in camp before lunch time,"
Jennifer's father said.

"I hope we didn't forget anything,"
her mother said. "We have apples,
beans, popcorn, and rolls."

"And sleeping bags," said Jennifer.
"And nuts for the chipmunks."

They went up steep hills and through
little valleys, and at last
there they were—under the pine trees,
in a beautiful camp.

"I'll open a can of beans right away,"
said Mrs. West.

"And I'll get out the rolls,"
said Mr. West.

Mrs. West looked in the bags and boxes.
"Where is the can opener?"
They all looked for the can opener.

A woman and a girl were sitting by a small tent.

"Hello," Jennifer's mother said. "I'm Kay West. We can't find our can opener. Do you have one we may borrow?"

"I'm Nan Chase," the woman said. "And this is Lisa. We all have to borrow something. We had to borrow a pan. Lisa, please get the can opener."

Soon apples, popcorn, and rolls were ready, and Jennifer's family and Lisa's family sat together to eat their lunches.

"I like the smell of the pine trees," Mrs. West said.

"I like the smell of smoke from the campfire," Jennifer said.

After lunch, Jennifer and Lisa went
all around camp. "Look!
Two rabbits!" Jennifer said.
She watched them hop away.

"And a snake!" said Lisa.
The snake slid under a log.

"But where are the chipmunks?"
Jennifer asked.

Almost as if he had heard Jennifer,
a little chipmunk came down from a pine
tree. Jennifer put a nut on the ground
for the chipmunk. "One for you,
and one for me, and one for Lisa,"
Jennifer said. The chipmunk sat up
on his back feet and ate the nut.

    While the girls were eating the nuts,
they saw a beautiful black and white animal
slowly making its way along the ground.

    "What was that?" asked Lisa.

    "I don't know," said Jennifer. "I've
never seen an animal like that before."

    Jennifer and Lisa looked all around
camp until time for dinner. When
Jennifer smelled campfire smoke, she knew
it was time to eat. So she and Lisa
hurried back together.

After dinner, all the people in camp sat and talked. They laughed and sang songs together.

Mr. West said, "God is so good. Let's thank Him for the trees and animals."

All the people prayed together to thank Jesus for many things.

"Tonight I'm going to leave the nuts by my sleeping bag," Jennifer said. "Maybe the chipmunk will come looking for them."

Jennifer got into her sleeping bag before dark and watched the stars come out in the sky. And then she went to sleep.

Sometime in the night, Jennifer heard something moving around. She sat up.

In the light of the moon, she saw the beautiful black and white animal again. It was creeping around her father's sleeping bag.

"Daddy," Jennifer said. "What is that animal?"

"Don't move," her mother said. "It's a skunk." Then the skunk went on its way.

"Is it gone?" Jennifer asked.

"I think so," said her mother.

"I HOPE so," said her father. "When I was little, I saw a skunk. It was afraid of me, and that skunk gave off a smell I can still remember."

72

The next morning, Lisa and Jennifer
talked about the skunk.

"It wasn't afraid of us," Jennifer
said. "But we were afraid of it."

The little chipmunk came near and sat
waiting. Jennifer gave him a nut.
"One for you, one for me, and one for
Lisa," she said.

It was almost time to start home.
"We have had such a good time together,"
Mrs. Chase said. "Maybe we can all come
back again sometime."

"Did you hear that?" Lisa said.

"I heard!" said Jennifer. "I'll write
to you. Maybe we can come back at
the same time."

"And I'll write to you too," Lisa said.

Then Jennifer and her mother and father
were on their way—back down steep hills
and through the small valleys.
And after a time, they were home.

74

The next day after school, Jennifer
decided to write to Lisa.

Dear Lisa,

Today, we all had
to talk about a good time
we remember. I talked
about you and the
chipmunk and the skunk.
When we all go back
to the mountains, I hope
our chipmunk will still be
there. But I hope the
skunk goes to another camp.
Write soon.

Love,
Jennifer
XXOOX

The Snake

A snake slipped through the thin green grass
A silver snake
I watched it pass
It moved like a ribbon
Silent as snow.
I think it smiled
As it passed my toe.

Karla Kuskin

Rosa and the Crow

From a branch in an oak tree,
a crow looked out over the neighborhood.
Near the tree, Rosa could see
Mr. Cid's back door.

Mr. Cid was at home by himself.
Mrs. Cid and their two children
were away.

"I wonder how he's getting along,"
Rosa thought.

Mr. Cid came out on the back step.
He had a red shirt and a spool of red
thread in his hands. He put them
down on the step.

"Hi, Mr. Cid," Rosa said.
"How are you getting along?"

"Everything's going all right,"
Mr. Cid said.

"I'm going to sit here in the sun
and mend a little rip in this old shirt
before I go to work. It's the only clean
shirt I have left."

The telephone rang. Mr. Cid ran
into the house to answer it.

Rosa heard a noise in the oak tree.
CAW—CAW—CAW
She looked up. The crow sat
on a low branch in the tree.
Then down it came with a swish.
And there it was—a beautiful crow
on Mr. Cid's step.

The crow picked up the spool of red
thread, and with a swish it was gone—
back to its branch in the tree.
Rosa watched. A bit of bark was
loose on the tree, and the crow
poked the thread under the bark.

Mr. Cid came outside.

"That was my wife," he said.

"She and the boys will be home tonight.

And NOW—I have to get busy.

It's almost time for work."

He sat down on the step
and picked up the shirt.

"Where's the thread?" he asked.

He looked on the step.

81

"Mr. Cid. . . ." Rosa said.

"I'm sorry. I don't have time
to listen," Mr. Cid said.
"I have to find that spool of thread."

"But Mr. Cid. . . ."

"It's almost time for your bus, Rosa,"
Mr. Cid said. "Why don't we talk
when we both have more time?"

82

Rosa looked up at the oak tree.
There was the spool of thread—
a small red dot in the green
oak tree. Mr. Cid was right.
It WAS almost time for the school bus.
So Rosa went down the street to wait for it.
She wondered what Mr. Cid would do.

Up in the oak tree, the crow sat
on a high branch and looked
out over the neighborhood.
CAW—CAW—CAW—

Workers and Tools

Match the workers with the tools they use in their work.

Draw pictures of tools these workers would use.

Which?

Look at the pictures. Can you answer the questions below?

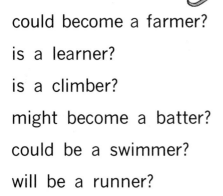

Which one or ones

could become a farmer?

is a learner?

is a climber?

might become a batter?

could be a swimmer?

will be a runner?

will grow taller?

is bigger than the others?

will never be smaller?

grows higher each year?

is greener in summer?

will not grow younger?

Make up questions of your own, using words that end in er.

Wild Creatures

How the Bear Got His Supper

There was no noise in the forest.
Rabbits hopped on soft little rabbit feet
in the wild grass, looking for their supper.
Chipmunks ran on soft little chipmunk feet
and ate their supper up in an old oak tree.
A little mouse came creeping . . . creeping . . .
There was no noise in the forest—
only the birds sang
in the top of the old tree.

And then, CRASH-BANG,
a bear—a big black bear—
came into the forest.
    The rabbits didn't move.
    The chipmunks were still.
    The mouse ran under a log.
    The birds called softly,
"Cheep . . . . cheep . . . ."

The bear stopped under the oak tree.

He was a hungry bear—a very hungry bear.

He looked up into the tree.

There in the oak tree was his supper—
a supper of fat acorns. But the acorns
were high—high up in the tree.

The hungry bear could not reach them.

But he knew how he would get his supper.

He climbed into the tree.

Up, up he climbed. But he did not reach
for the acorns.

He crawled out on a big branch of the tree.
He sat there and then he rocked the branch.
Up and down. Up and down.

And the branch broke with a CRASH-BANG.

Down they fell, branch and acorns
and big black bear. CRASH-BANG.

The bear rolled over. He sat up
and looked around. With his big, big paws,
he reached for the acorns.

He reached for more, and he ate his fill.

And while he ate his supper, the rabbits
and the chipmunks were still.

And only the birds called,

"Cheep . . . . cheep . . . ."

And when he was not hungry, the bear
went out of the forest with a crash and a bang.
CRASH-BANG.

And when he was gone, the rabbits looked
for their supper.

Chipmunks ran high up into the tree
and down again and hid acorns in the brush.

The little mouse came creeping . . . creeping . . .

Again there was no noise in the forest—
only the birds sang in the old oak tree.

Wild Things

On the side of a hill a little pack rat
is hunting for her supper. The pack rat
is hungry. And while she hunts, she is afraid—
very afraid—for the pack rat has many enemies.

And some of the pack rat's enemies are these:
Owl and Eagle, Fox and Bobcat, and

SNAKE.

Crawling—crawling, the snake is hunting
for his supper. He, too, is hungry.
And while he hunts, he is afraid, for the snake
has many enemies. And some of his enemies
are these: Owl and Eagle, Bobcat and

FOX.

The old fox barks at the moon. She is hungry.
She starts out to hunt for her supper.

She prowls over the hill and down again.

She prowls through the brush, and she is afraid.

When the fox was very little, she was afraid
of Owl and Eagle.

Now that she is old, she is afraid of

BOBCAT.

The bobcat prowls through the forest.

He prowls through the green forest
on big, soft feet. He makes no noise.

He is very hungry and he is afraid.

He is afraid of

PEOPLE.

Little Pronghorn

Alone, a little pronghorn lay waiting in the brush.

Far away, its mother ran across the open country.
A coyote was running after her. She led
the coyote far from the place where the
little pronghorn lay.

The coyote would not catch her for she
ran very fast—and no coyote could run
as fast as the mother pronghorn could run.

The little pronghorn lay very still.

Late that day a girl and her father
started for a ride. The girl saw the little pronghorn
in the brush. They stopped their horses.

"Where can its mother be?" the girl asked.

"I don't know," her father said, "but the
mother will not stay away long.
She will be back soon."

Then they heard the bark of a coyote
from far away. They heard the coyote bark again.

"The coyote is coming this way," the girl said.

"That coyote is prowling around looking for food.
He would like to find this little pronghorn here," her
father said. "We'll have to take the pronghorn with us.

The little pronghorn lay very still. The girl picked
it up and took it home in her arms. The little
pronghorn was only one day old, and it was
very small.

At home the girl gave the little pronghorn
some milk. It was very hungry.

Little Pronghorn was beautiful. It had
a red-brown coat. It had some white hair
on its face and around its tail and some
on its stomach. Its legs were very long.

"When Little Pronghorn stands up, its legs
look like sticks," the girl said. "Why did
God give it those funny little stick legs?"

"So Little Pronghorn can run fast,"
her father said. "It will learn to run by the time
it's about three days old, and soon it will run
faster than the coyote. Pronghorns can run faster
than all other animals in the land."

On the open grassland, when a pronghorn lies flat against the ground, it looks like the ground where it lies. Very soon it learns to lie flat against the ground. If a pronghorn lies very still without moving, and if it lies very flat, its enemies will not see it.

But sometimes it is afraid.

Around the pronghorn's tail is a ring of white hair. When a pronghorn is afraid, the white hair on its tail stands up in the ring. The ring of hair can be seen from far away, flashing white in the light of the sun.

It tells other pronghorns to watch for their enemies—to watch for coyote or eagle, prowling bobcat or mountain lion.

When a pronghorn is about three days old,
it can run and play.

So, very soon, when the girl raced her horse
down the road, Little Pronghorn raced with her.
It seemed to fly.

The day came when it was time
for Little Pronghorn to go back to the herd.

"A pronghorn is wild," the girl said.
"It must go back to the others
and live with the herd."

One morning when she rode her horse,
and Little Pronghorn raced with her,
she saw a herd of pronghorns.

The herd was standing on a far hill.

The little pronghorn knew the herd was there.
Its mother was with them.

Little Pronghorn ran fast, away
across the flat land and up the hill. The girl
watched it go. The pronghorn ran faster
than it had ever run before.

Little Pronghorn did not look back.
On it went—on and on, until it
was safe with the herd on the hill.

THE BEAVERS BUILD A HOUSE

The sun goes down and night will come soon.

Wild animals come softly from the woods.

They come to the pond to drink.

Two beavers swim across the pond.

It is time for them to go to work.

105

Beside the water are many young trees.
The beavers climb out of the water.
Each picks a young tree. And each stands
on its back legs and leans on its wide, flat tail.

They chew the bark of the young trees.
As they chew, chips fall to the ground.
The beavers chew almost through the trees.

A tree leans.

It leans a little more—

WHACK !

A beaver's tail hits the ground.

This is the beaver's way of saying DANGER.
   One of the young trees is about to fall,
and the beavers hurry away from the falling tree.
They hurry to the pond and dive deep down
into the water away from danger.

The tree falls to the ground.
It falls with a great CRASH !

After a while the beavers come to the tree
where it lies on the ground. They chew off
the branches. Now they stop chewing and listen
for danger. They listen for the coyote
and the bobcat.

The beavers take the branches
from the young tree to make a house.
They carry the branches out into the water
and put them in the mud down deep in the pond.
Again and again they carry branches.
In the pond, they make a pile of branches
that is higher than the water. The pile
of branches can be seen above the water.
This is the floor of their house.

111

They work many nights building this house.

They carry loads of mud in their front paws, then more and more loads.

They put mud on the floor of branches. They make a mud pile two feet high, on top of the branches. Then they put sticks and more mud on top of it all.

They dive deep under the water, and they dig two tunnels. These two tunnels go through the great pile of mud and branches to the place where their house will be.

They start to dig a cave in the mud. When they dig the cave, they carry loads of mud out through their tunnels.

At last they have a house to live in. They leave one little hole in the top of the house for air to come through.

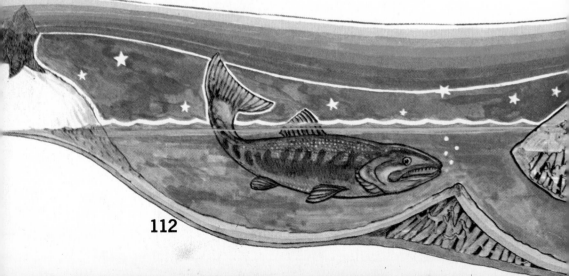

One side of the house is high,
and the other is low.

Their house is ready.

The beavers store food to last
all the winter long. Out through tunnels
they go for food. In through tunnels
they carry loads of branches.

They take the branches to the low side
of the house.

Here on the low side they will eat.

They will sleep and rest on the high
side.

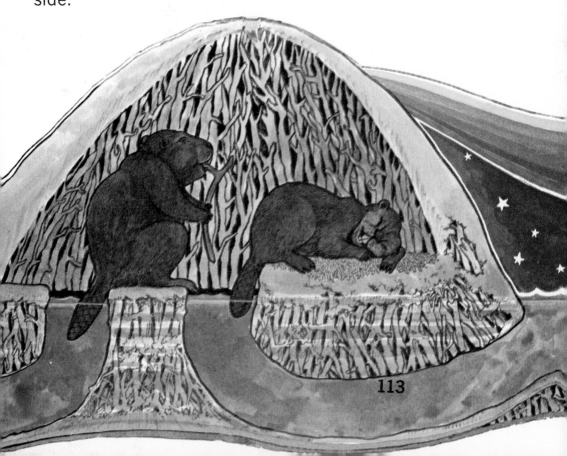

113

The nights are long, and snow falls.

Outside, far away, the bark of a hungry coyote is heard.

But in the beaver house two beavers are safe; safe from the coyote, safe from the bobcat, safe from all danger.

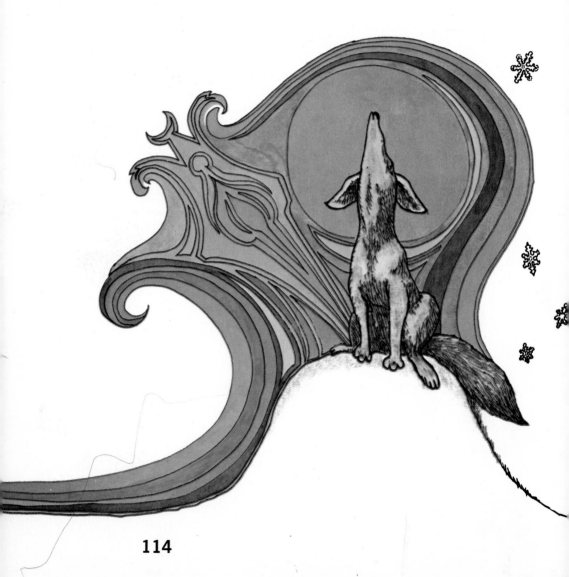

The Sea Otter

The sun comes up. A hungry otter
dives deep into the sea to look for her food.
Down she goes—down—

down.

She catches a fish and swims up with it.

Up—up through the water.

The otter floats on her back.

And she eats her fill.

The otter dives again, but this time she
is not looking for food.
She wants to find something to play with.
She finds a little rock, and she swims
up through the sea again.
Up—up through the green water.

She flips the rock into the air and she catches it. And if she drops it, down she goes after it, and she finds it and comes up again. The game goes on and on. And when at last, she is through with the rock, she lets it fall into the sea. And she plays with the otters in the herd.

They jump up from the water, high into the air. They flip over and over.
They jump again.

All day long, the otter plays and looks for food and plays again. Now she dives deep and she finds a clam.

The otter swims up with the clam
in one front paw, and a rock in the
other paw.

She floats on her back, and she puts
the rock on her stomach.

   She hits the clam against the rock, and she
eats bits of good food. A bit of clam shell
falls on her stomach. And the otter flips
over and over, and washes her stomach
in the sea.

Night comes, and the sea otter swims
to a bed of seaweed.
She pulls the seaweed around her.

She floats there on her back,
with seaweed for her bed.
She rocks with the tide, and she sleeps.

Animal Babies

Have you ever seen a baby animal just after it was born? Read about three kinds of newly born animal babies.

Black bear mothers have from one to four babies at a time. The babies are very small. New baby bears cannot see. They have no fur.

Baby chipmunks are born without fur. Their eyes are closed at first. There may be four or five in a family.

New baby rabbits have no fur and they are blind for a while. There may be from four to seven in a litter.

Ask your teacher to make a chart like the one on the next page. Then fill in the chart from the facts that you have just read.

	bears	chipmunks	rabbits
How many babies are born?			
Can the babies see when they are born?			
Are the babies covered with fur?			

Look at your chart when you have filled it in.
From the facts on the chart, which sentences
below could you say are true?

Rabbit, chipmunk and bear babies:

1. are born blind.

2. can run around right away after they are born.

3. are quite helpless at first.

4. have no fur at first.

5. play with each other right away.

6. are born without fur.

7. have brothers and sisters born at the same time.

126

Clickety-Clack

Song of the Train

Clickety-clack,
Wheels on the track,
This is the way
They begin the attack:
Click-ety-clack,
Click-ety-clack,
Click-ety, *clack*-ety,
Click-ety
Clack.

Clickety-clack,
Over the crack,
Faster and faster
The song of the track:
Clickety-clack,
Clickety-clack,
Clickety, clackety,
Clackety
Clack.

Riding in front,
Riding in back,
Everyone hears
The song of the track:
Clickety-clack,
Clickety-clack,
Clickety, *clickety,*
Clackety
Clack.

David McCord

Carmelita's Birthday

Carmelita knew exactly what she wanted for her birthday. Exactly. "Daddy," she said, "I know what I want for my birthday."

"And what is that?" asked her father.

"I'd like to have our family go somewhere together," she said.

"Where?" asked her brother, Ricardo.

"How about the aquarium?" Carmelita asked. "Remember when Grandma came to visit us and took us to the aquarium? I miss Grandma. Grandma always laughed a lot, and when Grandma laughed, I laughed too."

"I think it would be fine to go somewhere on your birthday," their father said. "Make up your mind where you want to go, Carmelita."

Carmelita thought about it. "I wouldn't mind going to the aquarium again," she said.

"Maybe a new place would be better," Ricardo said.

"Maybe," Carmelita said. She thought again. "I think I'd like to go to the airport," she said to her father.

"That's a great idea," said their father. "We'd all like that."

At last it was the morning of Carmelita's birthday. All of her family went to the airport. Carmelita watched the people who were waiting for planes. They were walking back and forth—back and forth.

A voice boomed out. The voice was telling about planes that were going and planes that were coming, but no one seemed to listen.

There were machines for everything.
Carmelita had popcorn out of one machine,
and Ricardo had peanuts out of another. Her
mother and father had apples out of another
machine. There were more machines than
Carmelita had ever seen in one place before.

Carmelita watched people who were getting off a plane. "There's GRANDMA!" she said.

"SURPRISE," said Ricardo. "We knew that Grandma was coming for a visit. It was a surprise for your birthday. But you picked the right place to go."

"I've got a secret," Carmelita said.

"What's the secret?" Ricardo asked.

"I was REALLY wishing to see Grandma too!" Carmelita said.

"Carmelita!" Grandma gave her a hug. "I couldn't stay away on your birthday. I had to get here in time to see you blow out the candles on your birthday cake."

"When I get ready to blow out the candles," Carmelita said, "you can help me!"

Grandma laughed. And Carmelita laughed too.

Lost and Found Department

William and his mother and father and their dog, Chips, lived on the first floor of an old brownstone house. They had lived there as long as William could remember. He liked the old house with big fireplaces to keep them warm.

And now the last of the brownstone houses in the block would be torn down, and there would be a big apartment house where the old brownstones had been.

Down the street was a big apartment house, where many of William's friends lived. "If we have to move, I'd like to live there," William said.

"I'd like to live there too," his mother said.

William's mother and father went down the street to talk to Mrs. Green about an apartment in her big apartment house.

"I'm sorry that your brownstone house is going to be torn down, and I would like to have your family," Mrs. Green said. "But you have that big dog. I don't want dogs in my apartment house."

After lunch William sat down to think. He was sorry that his own old brownstone house had to be torn down.

Fred Barber rode by on his bicycle. Fred lived in Mrs. Green's apartments, and William wished he could live there too. But he had to live where his dog could live.

Chips trotted off down the street.

Chips was a good dog. He didn't bark much, and he picked up all the litter that he found in the street. He picked up more than litter. He picked up everything he found in people's yards too!

William whistled for Chips.

Chips came trotting up, carrying a torn coat. He gave it to William.

"Thank you," William said. "This doesn't look exactly like litter." He looked at the coat. It belonged to Fred Barber. Fred had left it outside somewhere.

William went to Fred's apartment house and gave the coat to Fred.

He stopped and looked up at the apartment house. Then he thought to himself, "Chips and I make a good team. We are like a Lost and Found Department." He decided to talk to Mrs. Green.

Then he rang Mrs. Green's bell.

"Mrs. Green," he said. "I know you don't want dogs in your apartment house, but I'd like to live here. My dog would like it too. He knows this neighborhood."

"No," Mrs. Green said, "I don't want dogs in my apartment house."

"He is a GOOD dog," William said. "He doesn't bark much. He picks up all the litter he finds in the street. Your yard would always be clean. Chips would pick up every bit of torn paper—every bit of litter.

"He picks up things that are lost too. When he finds something, he comes carrying it to me, and I take it back where it belongs. We could be your Lost and Found Department."

Mrs. Green smiled. "So far, William, we get along very well without a Lost and Found Department."

William was not happy. He started home to his old brownstone house.

Chips trotted off by himself. After a while he came back with a toy bear. He gave the toy bear to William. William took it back to Jill Gray, and came home and sat on the steps of his old brownstone house.

When Chips came home again, he walked proudly, carrying a handbag. He gave it to William.

"Thank you," William said. He hurried inside his house. "Look what Chips found," he said to his mother. "It has money in it. It rattles!"

"Open it and see if there is a name inside," she said.

William opened the handbag.

"There is a lot of money here," he said. He looked and found a paper with a name on it. "It's Mrs. Green's!" he said.

William and Chips ran all the way to the apartment house.

Mrs. Green was standing on the front walk, talking to Mrs. Barber. "I don't know WHERE I could have left it," she said. "I was on my way downtown with the rent money, when I saw that my handbag was gone."

"Here it is!" William called.

"William," Mrs. Green said. "WHERE did you find it?"

"I didn't find it," William said. "My DOG found it!"

"Well," Mrs. Green said. "Well." She opened the handbag. "Everything is here." She looked at Mrs. Barber. "Mrs. Barber, I don't think the people in our apartment house would mind having ONE dog living here, do you?"

"I'd like to have a dog like Chips," Mrs. Barber said.

"William," Mrs. Green said. "Go home and tell your mother that I'd like to have your family here." She shut her handbag with a click. She patted Chips. "It will be a very good thing to have a dog here. I think that every apartment house needs a good Lost and Found Department," she said.

144

Red Tulips

Henry lived on the first floor of Mr. and Mrs. Camp's apartment house.

In front of the apartment house was a small garden.

In this garden Mrs. Camp had planted red tulip bulbs.

The tulip bulbs bloomed in the springtime.

Each springtime there were more and more tulips.

One fall when the tulips had stopped blooming, and their leaves were brown, Mrs. Camp said, "The tulip bulbs have multiplied. There are too many of them. I will take some of them out."

So Henry and Mrs. Camp dug up the tulip bed and raked it fine with a rake.

When they had planted the bulbs, many of them were left over.

"Now what shall I do with the tulip bulbs?" Mrs. Camp said.

"I would like to ask my friends if they want them," Henry said.

"Good," said Mrs. Camp. "Go and ask your friends."

Henry put the bulbs in a big basket.

He looked up at the apartment building.

On the second floor there were many window boxes.

Henry went up the steps and knocked at every door.

Everyone on the second floor was glad to have tulip bulbs for their window boxes.

On the next floor he knocked on Mr. Black's door.

"Would you like to have some tulip bulbs?" Henry asked.

And Mr. Black, who had no window box, said, "I'd be glad to have some tulip bulbs. Tulips always tell me that spring has come. I'll put them in pots and set them on my window sill."

When Henry got to the very top floor, he had only one tulip bulb left. On this top floor, Mrs. May lived alone.

"Would you like a tulip bulb?" Henry asked. "I'm sorry I have only one left."

"I don't have a thing to plant it in," Mrs. May said. "But I'm glad to have one bulb. I will FIND something to plant it in."

So all the people in the apartment house planted tulips that day.

Winter passed and then spring came.

With water and with sun, the bulbs grew in the little garden outside the apartment house.

With water and with sun, they grew in window boxes. They grew in brown pots.

First there were wide leaves, and then came the tulips.

In all the windows in that apartment house red tulips bloomed.

They bloomed in window boxes and in brown pots.

And on the very top floor in Mrs. May's apartment, one beautiful red tulip bloomed in a blue teapot.

All the neighbors saw the red tulips blooming there, and they knew that Henry was everyone's friend.

What's the Difference?

George lived on Cherry Street. Two girls lived next door. A boy and a girl lived down the street. And three boys lived across the street.

George went to the Adventist school on the other side of town, but the others went to the Cherry Street School.

George didn't like to talk much. He liked to read books.

George heard the children on Cherry Street talk. They talked about TV shows. They talked about movies. They talked about books George had not read.

Sometimes the children on Cherry Street played in the woods. They built tree houses and dug holes.

George liked to go to the woods too. But he liked to be quiet in the woods so that he could see the animals.

Dad asked George, "Why don't you play with the children on Cherry Street?"

"They are not like me," George told his father. "I don't know what to say to them."

"You could tell them about things you like to do," Dad said. "Maybe you could tell them what you see when you go to the woods."

"I just look at wild animals," George said. "Then I can tell a story about a wild animal for school. I don't think the children on Cherry Street would like that. They talk about different things."

George went outside. He started to walk to the woods. Then he saw the two girls from next door. He saw the boy and girl from down the street. He saw the three boys from across the street. They were all looking at him.

"We don't have anything to do," said the boy who lived down the street. "What are you doing?"

George looked down. He didn't know what to say.

"Where are you going?" called out one of the girls who lived next door.

George looked up. He started to answer. But then one of the boys from across the street said, "Can we come with you?"

George smiled. "I'm just going to the woods," he said. "But you can come with me."

All the children on Cherry Street went to the woods with George. They did not talk much.

George helped them see what the wild animals did. They watched a squirrel climbing a tree. They saw a rabbit hiding. They heard a crow cawing. And they saw a snake slipping through the leaves.

"I didn't know there were so many animals here," said one of the boys.

"I never heard so many animal sounds before," one of the girls said.

When George went home, Dad asked, "Do you have a story for school?"

"Yes," said George. "I can tell about a squirrel or a rabbit. I can tell about a crow or a snake."

"Did you learn anything new today?" Dad asked.

"Yes," said George. "I learned that I'm not much different from the other children on Cherry Street."

The Clover Street Trio

Jen and Linda and Kate lived on Clover Street. They were always together. Because they were three, everyone called them the Clover Street Trio.

They always walked to school together, and they came home together.

Then Jen would hurry out of her flat. Linda and Kate would hurry out of their apartment houses.

Some days one of the girls had three apples. Some days one would have three doughnuts. They were best friends and they liked Clover Street.

Some days they hunted in the clover that grew along the street.

"My grandmother says that four-leaf clovers make things special," Jen said.

"Clover Street is special," Kate said, "even if we never find a four-leaf clover here."

"If we want to skate our sidewalk is just right," Jen said.

"And we always want to skate," said Linda.

"It's good for jump-rope too," Kate said. Two held the rope and one jumped.

One morning there was a new girl in school.

Mrs. Lipman said, "This is Trudy. I hope everyone will be kind to Trudy."

"I'll show her where to put her coat," Johnny said.

"I'll show her where we keep our lunches," said Bob.

After school the Clover Street Trio sat on Jen's front steps, and they had a surprise.

The door of the apartment house across the street opened, and out came Trudy.

"Look," said Jen. "It's the new girl, Trudy."

"I guess she moved into the apartment," Kate said. "Do we want to ask her to play?"

No one answered.

"We can think about it after a while," Linda said.

"Let's skate," said Jen.

The Clover Street Trio skated up and down the block. They did not look at Trudy.

Trudy watched.

Jen and Linda and Kate jumped rope until Trudy went into her apartment house.

After Trudy went inside her apartment house, the Clover Street Trio sat on Linda's steps.

Linda sat with her chin in her hands. "I wonder how it would be if you and Trudy were the Clover Street Trio. I wonder how it would be if I watched," she said.

"I wonder," said Kate.

"Would we have more fun if we asked Trudy to play?" Jen asked.

"Maybe four would be better than three," Kate said.

The next morning Kate and Jen and Linda were waiting when Trudy and her mother came down their steps.

"Trudy can walk with us," Jen said.

"We will take her to school," said Kate.

"Thank you!" Trudy's mother said. She waved good-by to Trudy.

The four girls walked to school together.

"Do you have skates?" Linda asked.

Trudy nodded.

"Do you like to jump rope?" Kate asked.

Trudy nodded again.

"What do you have in your lunch bag?" Jen asked.

"Nuts for one thing," Trudy said.

"Trade you for an apple," said Jen.

When they reached the schoolyard, they all went inside together.

"Here comes the Clover Street Trio," Bob said.

"There can't be a trio with four people," said Johnny.

"We have a new name now," Kate said. "WE'RE the Four-Leaf Clovers."

One Will Do

Read the two sentences in each set. Then think of one word which fits both meanings.

1. If you ride in an airplane you do this.

   This is an insect which people do not like.

2. Most people do this to raw food.

   This is someone who wears a tall white hat and an apron.

3. When you do this, you lie down and turn over and over. This is the name of something you can eat for dinner.

One word will do for two of the pictures. Can you find the pictures that match?

Extending word meanings by finding words that fit two different meanings

What Is in the Block?

Read all the words around the block. Then read the sentence in the block. Think of a word that is like the other words and fits the sentence. What is it?

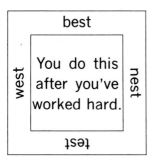

best

west | You do this after you've worked hard. | nest

test

lack

sack | Your foot makes one in the snow. | pack

crack

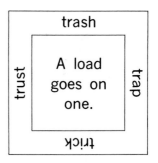

trash

trust | A load goes on one. | trap

trick

flake

flock | It comes from a fire. | flit

flash

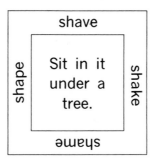

shave

shape | Sit in it under a tree. | shake

shame

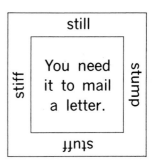

still

stiff | You need it to mail a letter. | stump

stuff

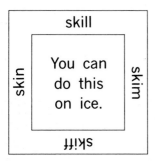

skill

skin | You can do this on ice. | skim

skiff

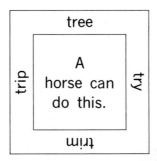

tree

trip | A horse can do this. | try

trim

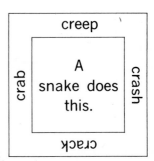

creep

crab | A snake does this. | crash

crack

A Question-
A Question

It's O.K.

Everyone in Mack's class knew about Teddy. If the class wrote a story, Mack wrote stories about Teddy. If the class drew pictures, Mack drew a picture of Teddy. When the class talked about pets, Mack talked about Teddy. Teddy was a horse. He was Mack's very own horse.

On Mack's birthday, the class came to his house to meet Teddy. Mack's mother made a big cake. His father let Mack's friends sit in the high seat of the bulldozer. He even showed them how it worked. But what everyone liked most was Teddy. Mack showed them Teddy's barn. He showed them what Teddy ate. He even showed them how to brush Teddy. Then everyone, two-by-two, rode Teddy.

How happy they were! Teddy stood very still to let each one climb up on his back. Teddy waited quietly until they were all set. Then he slowly followed Mack around the barn. When they got back, Teddy stopped right in front of the next two children.

169

Summer came and school was out. Now Mack could be with Teddy all day. Sometimes, Mack and Teddy walked side by side. Sometimes, they worked together. Mack would pick beans in the garden and Teddy would carry the beans to the house on his back. But most of the time, Mack rode on Teddy's back. They would ride and look. They looked at the birds, the sky, the fields—at all the things in God's beautiful world.

One day, when Mack was brushing Teddy, his mother called to him from the house.

"Mack! Mack! Would you come here, please? I have something to tell you," she called.

"Coming, Mother," said Mack.

"I'll be right back," Mack said to Teddy. Teddy moved his ears as if to say "O.K."

"I just got a call from Mr. Read," said Mother as Mack drew near.

"Mr. Read from Pathfinder's camp?" asked Mack.

"Yes," said Mother. "You know they don't have a horse at camp," she said. "So Mr. Read wants to know if you will let Teddy go to camp."

"You mean I can take Teddy with me when I go to camp?" asked Mack.

"Not exactly, Mack," she answered. "Mr. Read would like for the children to be able to ride Teddy all summer."

"But I will only be at camp for one week," said Mack.

"I know," said Mother.

Mack just stood there. Then he said, "Mr. Read wants me to let Teddy stay at camp all summer? Even when I'm not there?" he asked.

"Yes," said Mother. "After all, Mack, you have Teddy all the time. He's your horse. You can ride him whenever you want, but the other children don't have horses."

"NO!" said Mack.

"Mack," said Mother, "is that any way to talk to me?"

"I'm sorry, Mother," said Mack. "But it's just not fair to take Teddy away from me for the summer."

"All right, Mack," said Mother. "If that's how you really feel about it. Teddy is your horse and only you can let him go to camp. But before I call Mr. Read, why not think it over."

Mack ran back to Teddy and put his head on Teddy's neck. He was so unhappy. "Oh, Teddy!" he said. "They want to take you away for the rest of the summer."

Teddy turned and looked at Mack as if to say, "Don't be sad, Mack." Ever so slowly, Teddy began to move. Then he stopped, turned his head to the front and waited as if to say, "Let's go for a ride."

So Mack climbed up on Teddy's back and away they went through the fields. They went along slowly and quietly this way and that way. Mack looked at the sky, the birds, the trees, the fields all around him in God's beautiful world.

As they rode along, Mack began to think. He thought what it had been like before he had Teddy. He thought about how happy Teddy had made him. He thought about his birthday and how happy his friends had been when they rode Teddy.

"It won't be so bad," he said to Teddy. "After all, I'll be at camp a week. It's not that far away. I can come and see you." He looked down at Teddy. "When you are at camp, I can look for new things to see and new places to ride."

"Mother," said Mack as he came back into the house. "I have thought it over, and I have talked it over with Teddy." He smiled. "I've decided. You can call Mr. Read now," he said. "Tell him it's O.K. for Teddy to go to camp."

MICE

I think mice
Are rather nice.

Their tails are long,
Their faces small,
They haven't any
Chins at all.
Their ears are pink,
Their teeth are white,
They run about
The house at night.
They nibble things
They shouldn't touch
And no one seems
To like them much.

But I think mice
Are nice.

Rose Fyleman

Henry

On Judy's birthday she got many cards. One card was very different. It had money all over it.

The card said, "Buy something you want. With love, Aunt Ann."

"What can I buy?" Judy thought.

Judy took out the tithe. Then she said, "Would you take me to town, Dad? I'd like to go to Jay's Pet Shop."

"Not another pet!" said Father. "I should have guessed."

Judy and Dad went to see Jay at the pet shop. When they came home, Judy had a box in her hand. In the box was a little ball of white. It was a little white mouse!

"What is your little mouse's name?" asked Mother.

"His name is Henry," Judy answered.

"That box is too little for Henry," Mike said. "I'll make a house for him."

"Good," said Mother. "He needs more room to run around."

Mike got a big box. He put a screen on one side and on top. He put some sawdust on the floor. He made a little door. Then Mike made a sign over the door. It said, "Mouse House."

Judy took Henry out of the little box. She put him in his little house. "Do you like your house, Henry?" asked Judy.

Henry did not answer. He was running around in his little house.

"Maybe he would like something to eat," said Mother.

"What can he eat?" asked Mike.

Judy said, "Jay told us that Henry likes bread. He likes bird seed too. He can have a little nut or little bits of vegetables."

Judy fixed a little box in Henry's house for a bed. Mike fixed a drinking bottle with a tube. He put the bottle in the house.

"Henry can have water any time he wants it," said Mike.

Henry seemed to like the little house Mike made. He ran around in the sawdust. He had water. He had seeds and bits of vegetables any time he wanted them. And when he was tired, he went to sleep in his soft bed.

Judy taught Henry a trick. She taught him to eat from her hand.

Judy taught her little white mouse another trick. When she put food in his house, she rang a bell. Soon Henry knew what the bell was for. When Judy rang the bell, Henry came running.

Then Mike taught Henry a trick too. He put a little nut in one of his pockets. Henry sniffed and sniffed. Then he ran up into Mike's pocket to get the nut. After that Henry always knew where to get a nut.

One Sunday Mother was making pancakes. She put some batter in a pan. Some of the batter made a very little pancake.

"That one is for Henry," said Father. "That pancake is just right for Henry."

Judy went to Henry's house. She rang Henry's bell. Henry came running. He took the pancake from Judy's hand. He sat up and began to eat it.

After that, Henry had a little pancake every Sunday morning.

One day Father said, "Next Sunday we are going away. Who will take care of Judy's pets?"

"I'll take one pet," said Grandmother. "But I do not want to take care of the mouse. I do not like mice!"

"I'll take one pet," said Aunt Ann. "But I do not want to take care of the mouse. I'm afraid of mice!"

No one wanted to take care of Henry!

"We can ask Jay in the pet shop," said Mike to Judy. They went to the pet shop.

"I do not have room for his house," said Jay. "I will put him with the other mice."

"How will I know which one is Henry? They all look alike!" said Judy.

"We can put a red string on one leg," said Mike.

"Then you will know which mouse is Henry," Jay said.

Everyone was happy, and the family went away.

When Judy came back, she went to the pet
shop. She looked and looked. She looked at
every mouse. Not one had a red string on its
leg.

"Where is Henry?" asked Judy. "I don't
see any mouse with a red string!"

"He took the string off," said Jay. "He did
not like it."

"How will I know which one is Henry?"
asked Judy.

"You can have any mouse," said Jay.
"They are all the same."

"Oh, no," said Judy. "They are not all the
same. I want Henry."

When Judy told her family, they were all very sad.

"I know," Judy said. "I will get the bell. Maybe Henry will remember the bell."

"And I will make a very little pancake," said Mother.

Mike and Judy went back to the pet shop.

When Judy rang the bell, the mice were afraid. They ran to hide. All but one little mouse! He sat up. He sniffed and sniffed.

Mike opened the door. He rang the bell.

The little mouse came running. He took the pancake from Judy. He sat up and began to eat it.

Mike took the little mouse in his hand. The mouse ran up into Mike's pocket. "It IS Henry!" said Mike. "He is looking for his nut."

Henry went home in Mike's pocket. Soon he was in his little house, eating bits of vegetables. Everyone was happy.

"Next time we go away we will have to get a baby-sitter," said Father.

"Not a baby-sitter," said Mother. "A mouse-sitter!"

ONCE A FOREST

There's a whirring sound in the forest,
"Timber!" the voices call.
I hear the buzz of a busy saw
And the crack of trees that fall.

And now where once was a forest,
Are houses row on row.
I wonder about that forest.
Where did the animals go?

Patricia Miles Martin

Katie's Swimming Pool

Katie sat on the grass under a big tree. She was watching a bird splash in a puddle on the blacktop road. Her brother, Jordy, was working in his garden. "Look, Jordy," Katie called. "Watch the birds splash."

Just then a green truck came down the road. It stopped by the puddle. Three workers got out. One of them splashed the water out of the hole. The others began shoveling tar into the hole. They pushed the tar down and made it smooth.

"You wrecked the birds' swimming pool," called Katie.

The men laughed. "You'll have to make a pool for them," they said. Then they got in their truck and went on down the road.

"It's O.K.," Jordy said. "Come help me
pick the bugs off my beans. Mom said she
would take us to library when I'm finished.
We have some books to take back."

On the way to the library, Katie told Mom about the puddle. "What we need is a birdbath like Grandma has," Mother said. "But we don't have money for one."

"I know!" Katie said. "I'm going to find a book on birdbaths at the library."

Katie found three books. There were many pictures of birdbaths. She showed them to Jordy.

"Here's a pie-pan bath," said Katie.

"Mom won't let you use a pie pan," said Jordy.

"Here's a good one," Katie said. "It's made with a garbage can lid on a pipe."

"Don't be funny, Katie! Dad won't let you have the lid off our garbage can," Jordy said.

"I'll think of something," said Katie.

When they got home Jordy and Katie went into the building next to the barn. "This old pipe would make a good stand," Jordy said. "It's big on one end. Now what can we use for the pool?"

Katie walked around the yard looking.

What was that shiny thing over in the tall grass by the road? It was near where the puddle had been. She reached down and pulled out a hubcap.

"Oh, Jordy! Come here and see what I've found," she called.

"This hubcap is just the thing! Let's put it on top of the pipe," Jordy said. "We'll have a good birdbath."

The next morning Katie and Jordy looked out the window at the new birdbath. Some birds were splashing and drinking in their new swimming pool. Then three birds made a beeline for Jordy's beans and began picking off bugs.

"Would you look at that, Jordy," said Katie. "Our new pool is good for the birds and the birds are good for your garden!"

Vacation

It was only the first day of vacation, but already something was going on in front of Suzu's house. Suzu rushed outside. Her neighbor, Mrs. Bell, was looking up into an oak tree near the walk.

"What's in the tree?" Suzu said.

"It's Mike. A pet monkey," Mrs. Bell said. "I told my brother I'd keep it until after vacation. And wouldn't you know, the monkey's loose already. Already!"

Mrs. Bell had a little sack in one hand. She took one peanut from the sack. "Come on, Mike—come on."

Mike came down, grabbed the peanut, and climbed into the tree again. He curled his tail around a high branch and sat there, eating the peanut.

Mr. Sing came by. "What's going on?" he asked.

"A pet monkey is loose in the tree," Suzu said.

"I wish I could help," Mr. Sing said. "But I can't stop to catch a monkey. I have to catch a bus. Why don't you call the zoo? If he belonged to me, I'd take him to the zoo and leave him there."

Jill Brown came running down the street. "Did I hear that there's a monkey loose in that tree?" she said. "Let ME get him down."

Up she went. But the monkey went higher. When she could almost reach him, the monkey swung up to the branch above.

"This could go on all day," Mrs. Bell said.

Jill came back down the tree.

Then Suzu thought of something. "Can I have a peanut?" she asked.

"Take the sack," Mrs. Bell said.

Suzu sat down under the tree. She ate a peanut. "Yum. Good," she said.

Mike swung down to a low branch. Suzu ate another peanut. The monkey swung to the lowest branch and dropped to the ground. He hopped up on her lap. He put one long arm around her neck and dipped one little paw into the sack.

"Here's your monkey, Mrs. Bell," Suzu
said.

"Thank you, Suzu," Mrs. Bell said. "I'll
CERTAINLY be glad when vacation's over."

What Is the Secret?

Read all the words and phrases in each group. Can you find how they are all alike?

1. boat   coat   moan

    road   goat   roam

    soap   croak   foam

2. outside   a pounding

    a bounce   a round cloud

    flour   a house mouse

    pouting   loud sounds

    shouts   found a hound

How would *you* group these?

    knick knack   gladness

    glass   a knife

    gliding   knocking

    knowing   a glow

Make a list of things that are alike in some way. See if the others can guess your secret.

Using phoneme-grapheme correspondences to decode and categorize words

Can You Solve a Puzzle?

Make this on your paper

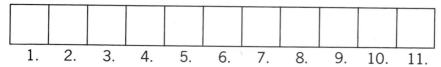

1. 2. 3. 4. 5. 6. 7. 8. 9. 10. 11.

Write in each square on your paper only the first letter of the following words in the order given and you will have the name of someone in your family.

1. This is an animal with a long, long neck.

2. This is an animal with a mask on its face.

3. Carmelita went there.

4. You hear this when many children play.

5. Stanley is one.

6. A cow gives this.

7. A kind of tree that a bear climbed.

8. Five and five make this.

9. In the summer the weather is this.

10. This is an animal with a trunk.

11. Some people carry an umbrella when it does this.

Who Cares?

The Littlest Girl

Mr. Gurney's coat flipped about in the cold wind. He pulled it up around his ears and walked to the house where Ellen was staying.

"Hello, Ellen," said Mr. Gurney. "I have a sailboat and plan to go to West's Island today. Would you and your sister like to go and see your friends there?"

Mr. Gurney stood by the fire and warmed his hands.

"Oh, yes. We would like to go," Ellen said. "We haven't seen the Hall family for a long, long time."

Ellen, Sarah, and Mr. Gurney walked down the hill to the boat. The wind pushed hard against them.

The boat was riding up and down in the water, its sails flipping in the wind.

"I think that sailboat is in a hurry to take us to the island," Ellen laughed.

"I hope so," said Sarah. "I want to get to the Hall's house soon. This wind is cold."

They climbed in the boat and started out. Ellen and Sarah pulled warm blankets around them. They watched sea birds turning in the air. They sang songs. They talked about things they wanted to tell the Halls.

Mr. Gurney smiled as he listened to Ellen and Sarah. But Mr. Gurney watched the clouds too. They were getting darker and darker.

Soon Mr. Gurney stopped smiling. He listened to the wind whistling harder and harder.

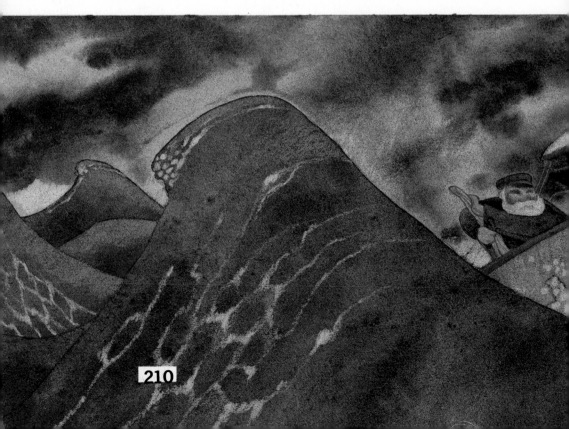

Ellen and Sarah stopped singing. They both stopped talking. They looked at the clouds. They listened to the wind.

And then—

Rain !

It poured down so hard that they could not see !

The sails flipped from side to side.

"This little boat could tip over," Sarah said.

"Get down in the boat," Mr. Gurney told them.

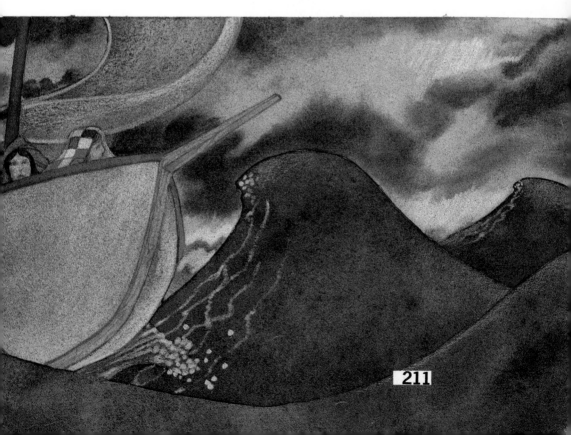

They all got down and pulled the blankets around them. "Jesus," Ellen prayed, "please save us."

No one could hear that prayer in the storm. Sarah didn't hear it. Mr. Gurney didn't hear it. But Jesus did. Jesus sent an angel to tell Ellen that she and Sarah and Mr. Gurney would be safe.

The boat rocked. The wind whistled. The cold rain poured down faster. But Ellen knew Jesus had a plan for them.

On the island the Halls were safe and warm. They did not know that anyone was coming to see them. So they all went to bed and pulled the warm blankets up over their ears.

But the littlest girl in the family couldn't sleep. She turned over and over until her blanket was all rolled up around her. "I must be the only one in the world who isn't sleeping," she thought.

She heard the whistling wind and the sounds of the rain coming down.

"—What's that!" She sat up.

She heard another sound. It sounded like someone calling.

"It must be the wind," she thought.

She pulled the blankets up over her ears.

"Oooh! There it is again," she said. "That's not the wind!" She jumped out of bed, hurried to the window, and opened it. Someone WAS calling for help!

"Father! Father! Wake up!" she called. "There must be a boat near the rocks!"

Mr. Hall hurried to the window. He heard a call. It seemed very far away.

Mr. Hall put on his raincoat and his tall boots.

He took his big boat out into the big waves.

Ellen, Sarah, and Mr. Gurney had been in the storm for a long time when Mr. Hall came. They were glad to get into Mr. Hall's big boat. "Thank God you heard our call for help," said Mr. Gurney.

"I didn't hear you. My littlest girl did," Mr. Hall said. "I don't know how she could hear with the wind and the rain pouring down. But somehow she did."

Soon they all were safe and warm in the Hall's big house. Mrs. Hall warmed some soup for Ellen, Sarah, and Mr. Gurney. The Hall children didn't wake up. They all had pulled their blankets over their ears. All but the littlest girl. She tiptoed down the stairs.

Mr. Hall saw her. "Come," he said. "Tell us, how could you hear in the storm?"

"I don't know," the little girl smiled. "I just couldn't go to sleep."

Then Ellen told everyone about the angel. "Jesus heard my prayer," Ellen said. "And He helped you hear us call," she smiled at the little girl.

"I'm GLAD I couldn't sleep," the little girl said as she gave Ellen a hug. "And I'm glad you're safe."

God Made Our Hands

God made our hands
to give and receive His blessings,
He made each voice
for singing a happy song,

God made our feet
to walk on a path of rainbows,
He made a smile
for smiling the whole day long.

God gave us eyes,
then filled all the world with beauty,
Sunshine and trees and stars above,
Wonderful child,
He gave us a gift so special
God gave us a heart
to share His love.

—*Jill Jackson and Sy Miller*

219

A New Tooth for Joseph

Joseph cried and cried. He cried because his mouth hurt, and he cried because his new tooth was broken.

He hadn't meant to break his tooth. He just fell down while he was playing ball. Then his mouth hurt, and his new tooth was half gone. So Joseph cried.

Joseph ran home, but he couldn't tell Mother what was wrong. He just cried with his mouth open and she saw the broken tooth. She looked at Joseph's mouth and went right to the telephone.

"Hello," she said. "Can the dentist see Joseph right away?... He's broken his front tooth . . . Thank you . . . We'll be right there." She hung up the telephone.

Joseph had been to the dentist before to get his teeth cleaned, but he was afraid now.

He had heard his friends at school talk about the dentist. "The dentist's office scares me," they said. "It always hurts when I go to the dentist." So Joseph cried.

"Here we are," Mother said, as they walked together into the office. They went into a nice cool waiting room. There were some good books to read. Joseph had just opened a book when a lady said, "Joseph, the dentist will see you now."

Joseph was scared. He was too scared to cry. He went into a room with many shiny machines. "Sit here," the lady said. "The dentist will be here soon. She'll use these machines to help fix your tooth."

Joseph grabbed the arms of the chair and waited.

"Hello," the dentist said as she came into the room. She had on a white coat. She smiled. She had pretty white teeth.

She looked into Joseph's mouth. She talked to him about what she was going to do. She showed him how the machines work. She even fixed a little mirror so Joseph could watch.

When the dentist was all done, Joseph had a new tooth. "You'll have to come back," the dentist said. "This tooth will stay in your mouth until we make a good strong tooth for you. But you can smile all you like and no one will ever know you had a broken tooth."

"Thank you," Joseph said. "I'll be back."

He went to the waiting room. "Well," Mother said. "You are not crying now." Joseph smiled. "What a nice smile you have," Mother said. Then Joseph laughed and let all his teeth show.

Automobile Mechanics

Sometimes
I help my dad
Work on our automobile.
We unscrew
The radiator cap
And we let some water run—
Swish—from a hose
Into the tank.

And then we open up the hood
And feed in oil
From a can with a long spout.
And then we take a lot of rags
And clean all about.
We clean the top
And the doors
And the fenders and the wheels
And the windows and floors. . . .
We work *hard*
My dad
And I.

    —*Dorothy Baruch*

No Smiles Today

Jimmy's sister seemed to smile all the time. She was just a happy baby. She did cry now and then, but soon she stopped and smiled.

One day, Jimmy came home from school and ran into the house.

"Hi, Dad. How is my little sister with the big smile?" he asked. "You both look a little sad today."

"I'm glad you're home," said Dad. "Your baby sister is not smiling today. She's crying and crying. I know what's the matter. Her mouth hurts. Her teeth are starting to come in."

"I see she's putting her hand in her mouth," said Jimmy. "Did you try holding her and singing to her?"

"That didn't help much," said Dad.

"Did you try taking her for a ride in the stroller?" Jimmy asked.

"A ride in the stroller didn't help her," said Dad. "Those teeth hurt a lot."

"How about putting her in her playpen with her toys," said Jimmy.

"See for yourself. She just holds on to the sides and wants to get out," said Dad. "But, you can see she's getting steady on her feet. Soon she will let go of the sides and stand alone."

"I know how she's feeling," said Jimmy. "When I fell and hit my head, it hurt for a long time. Nothing made me feel like smiling when my head hurt."

"Maybe you can help, Jimmy," said Dad. "I haven't read all these papers yet. They're very long, and I should mark them for my class tonight. We're going to eat as soon as Mom gets home from work. We're having spaghetti. I've fixed the sauce, but I haven't started to cook the spaghetti yet."

"You're asking the right one to help," said Jimmy. "You're good at cooking and marking papers. One thing I'm good at is getting my baby sister to smile. We both have work to do."

"First I will try my funny faces," thought Jimmy. It seemed to be working. The baby looked up and stopped crying.

"I know," said Jimmy. "Today in school we read about how to make paper hats. How would you like me to make one for you?"

Jimmy put some paper on a chair. With steady hands, he made the paper into a hat. The baby was looking at what he was doing. She didn't think about her teeth. He put the hat on his head. She smiled a little. He put the hat on her head. She smiled a lot. Then she started to laugh.

Just then Dad came into the room. "The spaghetti is ready," he called. "My job is done and it looks like yours is too."

Maxie

That Was Thursday

Maxie lived in three small rooms on the top floor of an old brown house on Oak Street. She had lived there for many years, and every day was the same for Maxie.

Every morning, seven days a week at exactly seven o'clock, Maxie raised the shades on her three front windows.

Every morning at exactly 7:10, Maxie's big orange cat jumped up to the windowsill and fell asleep in the morning sun.

At 7:20, if you were watching Maxie's back window, you would see her raise the shade to the very top. Then she uncovered the bird cage that was hanging near the window. The little yellow bird inside the cage began to sing, t-r-r-r-r-r, tweet. It was 7:22.

At 8:15 every morning, Maxie's door opened with a tired squeak, sque-e-e-e-k, sque-e-e-e-k. Then down the steps she went to the front door. Her newspaper was just outside.

Maxie always tried to reach for the paper while she held the door open with her foot. But the paper was too far away and the door always closed before she got back inside.

So, at 8:20 every morning, Maxie rang Harvey's bell, and Harvey would open the door and let Maxie in. It was Harvey who took care of the building.

Only Maxie knew what she ate for breakfast, but everyone knew she had sassafras tea. At 8:45 every morning, the whistling of her teakettle made dogs bark, cats meow, and babies cry. And when it stopped it was 8:46.

The mailman knew more about Maxie than anyone.

He knew she had a sister in Grand Island who sent her a birthday card every year.

He also knew that Maxie planted flowers in her window boxes. Every spring he delivered the seeds.

At nine o'clock every morning, Maxie went down the steps again. This time she went outside and put her small bag of garbage in the can.

Then she came back in and waited for the mailman. She would watch as he put the mail in the boxes for the other people in the building.

Again she climbed the steps. Maxie went into her apartment and the door closed with the same tired squeak.

One day at 1:05, just as she did every day at 1:05, Maxie moved the bird cage with the yellow bird in it to the front window. It was cool there now.

Her big, orange cat moved to the back window.

"You are happy to be there, day after day," Maxie said to the cat. "All you ever want to do is move from one window to the other. You don't need anyone, and no one really needs you. You don't seem to care."

Maxie sat down. "I care," she said. "I'm not a cat, but I could just as well be one." Maxie was tired. She went to bed.

That was Thursday.

On Friday

On Friday morning at seven o'clock, all the shades on Maxie's windows were still down. At 7:10, the big, orange cat was still asleep at the foot of Maxie's bed. The bird never sang, no footsteps were heard on the steps, and the teakettle didn't whistle.

At nine o'clock, the mailman came. He had seeds for Maxie, but this morning she was not there. He decided to take the seeds to her door.

He climbed the steps. He knocked and waited. There was no sign of Maxie.

At 9:03, Mr. David, who lived on the third floor, came hurrying up the steps.

At 9:05, Mr. and Mrs. Gomez got there from across the street.

At 9:07, Mrs. Temple came over from next door.

Suzu Kim came up at 9:10 with her little brother.

Five people from the family who lived on the second floor, made it up by 9:13.

Then came Harvey, who worked in the building.

By 9:17, a crowd of people, three dogs, and two cats, all waited for Maxie to open her door.

And when she didn't, they all went in. They found Maxie in bed. Someone called Doctor Bell. By the time he got there, at least fifty people were crowded into Maxie's small living room.

When Doctor Bell came out of Maxie's bedroom, he looked at all the worried faces.

"Maxie isn't really sick," he said. "She is lonely. She doesn't feel loved. She doesn't feel that anyone needs her."

No one answered until Mrs. Temple marched past Doctor Bell right into Maxie's bedroom. "Maxie," she said, "you let me down. You and your yellow bird let me down!

"Every morning at 7:22 your bird wakes me up. Then it's my job to wake my family. Mr. Temple makes the breakfasts at the diner, and because of you he is still asleep. Why, there must be at least seventy-five people at the diner waiting for their breakfasts."

Everyone gathered around Maxie's bed. Maxie sat up and listened to what they had to say.

"I couldn't go to school this morning," said Suzu Kim. "I missed my bus because your teakettle didn't whistle."

"The school bus never came this morning," said Mr. David who drove the bus. "I didn't wake up in time. I never heard Sandy Small's footsteps over my head."

Sandy always got out of bed when she heard Maxie's door squeak. People were waiting for her right now at her bookstore.

Mr. and Mrs. Gomez both had important jobs. Their clock was Maxie's window shade. This morning they missed their train.

Harvey said he hadn't cleaned the front steps. Because Maxie didn't ring his bell, he was late getting started.

They all decided that there must be about four hundred people who needed Maxie—or who needed someone who needed Maxie—every morning.

Maxie smiled. She got out of bed and made five pots of sassafras tea. Each time the kettle whistled, dogs barked, cats meowed, and babies cried.

Maxie listened and thought about how many people were being touched by these sounds—her sounds. By 9:45 that morning, Maxie had fixed sassafras tea for everyone, and she was so pleased.

Helping People

There are helpers all around you. You can see a policeman helping people who are lost. You can see a checker helping people in the store. You can see neighbors helping each other. You can see ways that God helps people too.

When you see a mailman on the corner, you may not stop to talk to him. But you may imagine what he is thinking and doing. Maybe he is hungry. Maybe he is hot.

Here is a picture of some helping people. Try to imagine what the family may be thinking, saying, and doing. Then write a story about the picture.

245

Old and New Ways of Saying Things

When things have been said the same way many times they lose their freshness. Stale sayings are called clichés. Can you think of some? Tell the missing word in these clichés.

1.

High as a house

Quiet as a ____

2.

Bold as brass

Clear as ____

3.

White as a sheet

Red as a ____

4.

Blue as the sky

Nice as ____

Now think of a new fresh way to say an old phrase. Instead of saying "cool as a cucumber" you could say "cool as an ice cube on a hot summer day." Try saying these in your own way.

Black as coal

White as a ghost

Warm as toast

Light as a feather

Fox and the Fire

Fox and the Fire

The young red fox stood near a cave on the side of a mountain.

For three days, a strange smell of danger had come with the wind. Now with the smell of danger, came the good smell of rabbit.

And the young red fox was hungry.

She started out to catch her supper.

She made no noise.

Close by, a gentle rabbit nibbled a weed.

The fox saw it and crept close.

Before the fox could catch her supper, a blue jay came low and screeched in anger, and the rabbit flashed into its burrow.

The fox whimpered, and sniffed at the burrow and scratched at the earth.

And even as she whimpered, gray-black smoke came heavy with the wind. Far away, in the forest, fire crawled along the ground and dry leaves snapped and crackled in its path.

The fox heard the roar of fire leaping from one tree to another, and she knew she must run.

At first she was bewildered and did not know which way to go.

Rabbits and mice came from their hiding places. Squirrels darted along the ground and quail called from the greasewood.

Two squirrels ran by and the fox followed behind them.

Sparrows and blue jays flew low overhead as the crackle of fire came closer.

Together, the animals ran out of the forest and the fox forgot that she was hungry.

On they went, across green fields until they came to a road.

The fox followed beside the road.

She came to a low brown house with a big tree growing beside it.

Beyond the tree was a barn.

Between the barn and the house was a pen, and inside the pen, a small chicken house.

With the strong, close smell of chicken came the smell of human and dog.

The fox shivered, ready to run, but there was no place to go.

Inside the house, a dog barked wildly, and the fox ran to the barn. Under the barn she found a small hole where she could hide.

She lay there——her nose on her paws—— watching——

Rabbits and chipmunks, squirrels and mice, found hiding places. Squirrels and chipmunks went up in the tree, and rabbits and mice under the house.

Five deer came, and lay down close beside the barn.

The fox felt the shake of the earth when the fire trucks rolled up, their red lights flashing and their sirens screeching.

Cars came with people to help fight the fire. With shovels and spades, they turned the earth. Tanker trucks came and a fire fighting bomber flew low overhead.

Inside the house, the dog howled like a wild animal.

In the hours that followed, the fox huddled small in her hiding place.

The people at the ranch fought the fire with the fire fighters, and the fire was held back. The house, the barn, and the tree were saved.

When the fire was out, all the people went inside the house, and the fox remembered that she was hungry.

She crept from under the barn and went up to the house.

Through a window she saw a big black dog, walking back and forth.

The fox crept toward the road. When the earth was cool, she trotted back over the black fields.

The fox found her cave on the side of the mountain, but the leaves and grass were burned and the mountain was bare.

She hunted for her breakfast, but the rabbits and the mice had gone to new hiding places and the fox found nothing.

She hunted all day, and when night came, she started out across the black fields.

When she reached the ranch, she stopped. There was no sound from the low brown house.

The fox crept toward the chicken house.

With a mighty leap, the thin, hungry fox was over the fence.

Without making a sound, she went into the chicken house.

255

She reached up and seized a chicken. With one quick shake of her head, it was dead.

The chickens set up a great squawking, and the fox leaped up and over the fence and away.

The door to the house opened. People shouted and a dog barked. Then the dog came leaping through the doorway.

The fox ran toward the road.

She galloped along beside the fence.

The bark of the dog was close—closer—

The fox leaped to the top rail of the fence and waited there in the dark.

256

The dog did not see her,
and went racing by.

The fox went on along the top of the fence.
Far away, she could hear the bark of the dog.

Back in the barnyard, the dog trotted
around the chicken pen, and chickens scolded
softly and settled down again to sleep.

The fox did not return.

257

In the days that followed, seeds were planted in the burned earth, and clover and wild grass grew again.

In the forest, new branches grew green, and little animals found shelter in trees and in burrows.

258

The fox hunted for her supper.

And when she had eaten, she lay safe in her cave, and she cleaned her fur and pulled the burrs from between her toes.

When the moon rose low over the valley, she went outside and rolled in the dirt and shook herself.

She pointed her nose toward the moon and howled.

From far away, she heard a bark—a warning bark.

Far down in the valley, the black dog was answering her call.

The fox sniffed the air, and she smelled the good, cool, damp smell of green growing things, and trotted off into the forest.

New Words in this Book

The following new words are presented in *Love Your Neighbor,* Level seven, Life Series Readers. Words listed with underscores are new enrichment words. Those words listed without underscores are new basic words. Because of the large number of decodable words in this book, they are not listed here. Decodable words for each selection are listed in the Teacher's Edition.

UNIT 1

Page

8   Bradleys
    move
    William
10 front
    Stanley
    pleased
12 climbed
    oak
    higher
13 almost
15 having
    gardens
    better
17 umbrella
18 through
19 decided
    proudly
20 cloud
22 drop
    knew
23 won't

    own
24 listened
    swish
    hurried
26 hair
    hurry
    Pathfinder
27 bicycle
    barber
    push
    ahead
    gone
28 shoe
29 three
    chair
31 hurried
    most
32 telephone
    camp
    worried
    until
33 care
    while

34 across
36 crawled
    pushed
39 flip
40 exactly
    against
    held
41 tail
    any
42 pleased
43 puppy

UNIT 2

48 Jonathan
    paint
49 parade
    stomach
    curled
    beetles
50 robin
    head
    worm
    ground

51 slow
    won't
54 world
    kinds
    those
55 hogan
    beautiful
56 quail
    cactus
    quietly
57 rattle
58 language
60 pail
    field
    thirsty
62 coyote
63 lunch
    anything
    apples
    rolls
    chipmunks
64 valleys
    can opener

262